ISBN 0 86112 430 8
© Brimax Books Ltd 1987. All rights reserved.
This edition published by Brimax Books Ltd, Newmarket,
England 1992.
Reprinted 1993
Printed in Spain.

THE ADVENTURES OF DRAGON

BY LUCY KINCAID

ILLUSTRATED BY ERIC KINCAID

Contents

BRIMAX BOOKS · NEWMARKET · ENGLAND

DRAGON in THE WOOD

It is a hot day.
The birds are asleep.
The bees are asleep.
The rabbits are asleep.
All the animals are asleep.
Only the flowers are
awake.

The birds wake up.
The bees wake up.
The rabbits wake up.
All the animals wake up.
"What is that?" they say.

"Who is coming?" say the
birds.
"Who is coming?" say the
animals.
"It is a dragon," say the
bees.
The animals are afraid.
They all hide.
The flowers do not hide.

They all look at the
dragon.
The dragon is hot.
He sits down.
They can all see the
dragon.
The dragon cannot see
them.
They are hiding.

What will the dragon do?
The dragon shuts his eyes.
The dragon opens his
mouth.
The dragon begins to sing.
They do not like the
dragon's song.
They all want him to stop
singing.

They all come out of
hiding.
"Stop!" say the birds.
"Stop!" say the bees.
"Stop!" say all the
animals.
The dragon stops singing.

The dragon opens his eyes.
"Where have you come
from?" says the dragon.
"We live here," say the
birds.
"I did not see you," says
the dragon.
"We were all hiding," say
the bees.

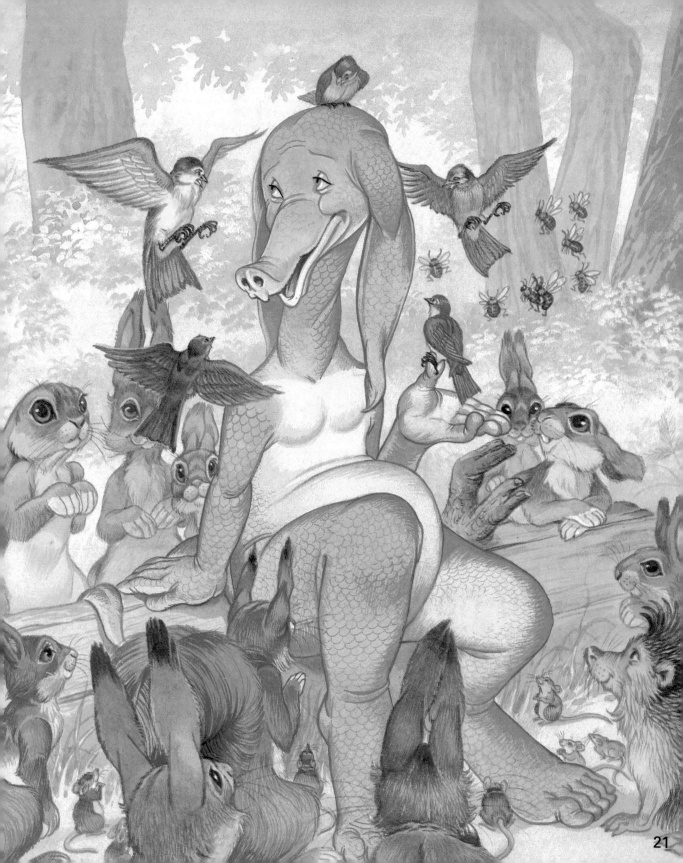

"Can I sing a song for
you?" says the dragon.
"No! No! Please do not
sing," they say.
The dragon looks sad.
"Nobody will let me sing,"
he says.
The dragon begins to cry.
They have never seen a
dragon cry.

"Are you a real dragon?"
they say.
The dragon shows them
that he is.
He puffs smoke.
He spits fire.
They are all afraid.
They all run away.
"Come back," says the
dragon. "I will not hurt
you. I just want to sing."

25

"We will help you," say
the birds. "Listen to us."
The dragon listens to the
birds.
The dragon opens his
mouth. He tries to sing like
the birds. He cannot. He
puffs smoke. He spits fire.
"Stop!" say the birds.
"Stop!" say the bees.
"Stop!" say the animals.

The dragon is sad. He walks away.
"Come back!" say the animals.
"We will help you," say the bees.
"How?" say the birds.
"Bees cannot sing."
"We can hum," say the bees.
"Humming is like singing."
The bees begin to hum.

"Can I do that?" says the
dragon.
"You can if you try," say
the bees.
The dragon tries to hum.
He can do it. He can hum
just like the bees. "Hum
hum hum," hums the
dragon.
Nobody tells him to stop.
"Hum   hum   hum," says
the dragon.

H-M-M-M-M-M-M-M-M

H-M-M-M-M-M-M-M

H-M-M-M-M-M-M-M-M

Dragon is humming a
song.
The bees are humming too.
The birds are singing.
The animals join in.
The rabbits tap their feet.
The flowers nod their
heads.
They are all happy.

HM-MM-MM-MM-MM-MM

HM-MM-MM-MM-MM-MM

Say these words again

listen	spits
mouth	their
asleep	join
animals	nobody
hiding	singing
afraid	hurt
humming	flowers

What are they doing?

sleeping

sitting

puffing

tapping

nodding

DRAGON'S HIDING PLACE

Dragon lives in the wood.
The bees are his friends.
He hums songs with them.
One day, Rabbit comes to
see them.

HM–MM–MM–MM–MMM

HM–MM–MM
HM–MMM–MM
HM–MM–MM
HM–MM–MMM

HM–MM–M
HM–MM–MM–MM
HM–MM–MM–MM
HM–MM–MMM
HM–MM–MMM

Rabbit looks sad.
"Oh dear," says Rabbit.
"What is it?" says Dragon.
"What is it?" say the bees.
"There are men in the
wood," says Rabbit.
"What do they want?" say
the bees.
"They want Dragon," says
Rabbit.

Dragon goes with Rabbit.
The bees go with Rabbit.
They see the men.
They hide behind a tree.
They watch. They listen.
The men have a net.
"We will catch the
dragon," say the men. "We
will put the dragon in a
cage."

Dragon is afraid.
"What can I do?" says
Dragon.
"You must hide," says
Rabbit.
It is too late. The men see
Dragon. They run after
him.
Rabbit gets under their
feet. He trips them up.
The bees buzz round the
men.
Dragon gets away.

Dragon looks for a place to hide. He sees a hole in a tree.

Dragon gets into the hole.

"What are you doing in the tree?" says Badger.

"I am hiding," says Dragon.

"I can see you," says Badger.

"What can I do?" says Dragon.

"Men are coming. They
want to put me in a cage,"
says Dragon.
"I will help you," says
Badger.
Badger rolls logs in front of
the hole.
Nobody can see the hole.
Nobody can see Dragon.
Badger goes on his way.

The men come. They have
a net. They have sticks.
"Where is that dragon?"
say the men.
Dragon keeps very still.
The men do not see him.
The men go away.

It is safe. Dragon can come out.
Where is Dragon hiding?
Nobody knows.
The animals look for Dragon.
Nobody can find him.

Dragon is still inside the
tree. He knows it is safe to
come out.
He cannot get out.
He cannot move the logs.
"I will shout," says
Dragon. "The animals will
hear me."

Dragon opens his mouth.
But he knows he must not
shout.
He is a dragon. Dragons
spit fire when they shout.
Fire will burn the tree.
"I know what to do," says
Dragon.

Dragon begins to hum.
He hums as loud as he
can.
"Hum   Hum   HUM   HUM."
Dragon's friends hear the
humming.
"Only Dragon can hum like
that," say the bees. "He
must be inside the tree."

HM-HM-MM-MMM-MMM-MM-MM-MMM

They try to move the logs.
They cannot.
Badger comes to the tree.
Badger wants to help
Dragon.
"There is nobody in that
tree," says Badger.
"Yes, there is," says
Rabbit. "Dragon is in the
tree. We can hear him
humming."

"Dragon is our friend," say the bees. "It is safe for him to come out now."
"Then I will help you," says Badger.
They roll the logs away from the hole.
Dragon gets out.
"I am glad to see you all," says Dragon.
"And we are glad to see you," say his friends.

Say these words again

watch   sticks

loud   nobody

catch   shout

cage   fire

their   Badger

buzz   afraid

only   knows

What are they doing?

hopping

running

hiding

falling

helping

DRAGON and SLEEPY OWL

Dragon lives in the wood.
He has many friends.
Owl is Dragon's friend.
Owl is on his way home.

Owl has been out all night.
He has been very busy.
Owl is very tired. He goes
to sleep. Along comes Fox.
"Wake up, Owl," says Fox.
"I want to talk to you."
Owl wakes up.
He listens to Fox.

Fox has gone. Owl is
asleep. Along comes
Rabbit.
"Wake up, Owl," says
Rabbit. "I want to talk to
you."
Owl wakes up.
He listens to Rabbit.

All the animals want to
talk to Owl. Owl is very
tired. He cannot work day
and night.
He must get some sleep.
Owl goes to see Dragon.

"Will you stand under my tree?" says Owl. "Will you see that no one comes to talk to me? I must get some sleep."
"I will come now," says Dragon.
Owl goes back to his tree. Dragon stands under the tree.

A mouse comes to see
Owl.
Dragon growls.
The mouse runs away.
A squirrel comes to see
Owl.
Dragon growls.
The squirrel runs away.
Dragon growls when
anyone comes near the
tree.

"Are you asleep, Owl?"
says Dragon.
"No," says Owl.
"Why not?" says Dragon.
"Your growls keep me
awake," says Owl.
"I am sorry," says Dragon.
"What can I do?" says
Dragon.

The bees know what to do.
They know a sleeping
song.

"Hum   Hum   Hum," hum
the bees. "Close your eyes.
Go to sleep.

Hum   Hum   Hum."
Dragon hums too.

"Hum   Hum   Hum," hums
Dragon. "Close your eyes.
Go to sleep.

Hum   Hum   Hum."

Owl's eyes are shut.
Owl is asleep.
"Do not stop humming,"
say the birds. "Owl will
wake up if you do."
Dragon keeps on humming.
So do the bees.

HM-MM-MM-MM-MM

HM-MM

HM-MM

MM-MM-MM-MM-MM-MM-MM-MM

85

The animals listen to the song. They get sleepy. The birds listen to the song.
They get sleepy.
Soon they are all asleep.

HM-MM-MM-M

HM-MM-MM-M

HM-MM-M-M-M-M

The bees are awake.
The bees are still
humming.
Dragon is still awake.
Dragon is still humming.
The bees are getting
sleepy. Dragon puts his
paws over his ears.

HM-MM-MM-Z

HM-MM-MM-MM-MM

HM-MMMM-MM-M

M-MM-M-MM-M-M

The bees are asleep.
Dragon is still awake.
His paws are over his ears.
Dragon cannot hear the
sleeping song.

Owl wakes up.
"I cannot hear anyone,"
says Owl.
Dragon tells him they are
all asleep.
Owl laughs when he sees
them asleep. Owl laughs
so much that they all wake
up.
And then they all laugh
too.

Say these words again

busy	work
friends	night
listen	sleepy
eyes	sorry
talk	paws
tired	laugh
squirrel	growls

What are they doing?

sleeping

standing

laughing

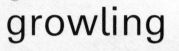

running

growling

DRAGON and THE RABBITS

Dragon lives in the wood.
He hums songs with the
bees.
The baby rabbits want to
hum too. They do not
know how to hum.

Dragon stops humming.
"Go away, and play," says
Dragon.
The bees stop humming.
"Go away, and play," say
the bees.
The baby rabbits hop
away.
They hop into the wood.

Dragon is humming again.
The bees are humming again.
Along comes Mother Rabbit.
"Where are my babies?" says Mother Rabbit.
"I do not know," says Dragon.
"We do not know," say the bees.

HM-MM-MM-MM-MM-MM

HM-MM-MM-MM-MM

HM-MM-MM-MM-MM-MM

Mother Rabbit calls her
babies. They do not come.
Mother Rabbit begins to
cry.
"I have lost my babies,"
she says.
"Do not cry," says Dragon.
"We will find your babies
for you," say the bees.

They all look for the baby rabbits.
Dragon looks for them.
The bees look for them.
Mother Rabbit looks for them.
The baby rabbits have gone.
Nobody can see them.
"They must be hiding," says Dragon.

Dragon stops. He stands still.

"Listen," says Dragon. "I can hear something."

"So can I," says Mother Rabbit.

"So can we," say the bees.

Dragon peeps over the
bush.
He can see something.
"Come here," says Dragon.
The bees look over the
bush.
Mother Rabbit looks over
the bush.

The baby rabbits are
sitting on the grass.
"What are they doing?"
say the bees.
The baby rabbits are trying
to hum.
They are trying very hard.
But they cannot do it.

"Hallo!" says Dragon.
"What are you trying to
do?"
The baby rabbits see
Dragon.
They hop away and hide.
"Come out of there," says
Dragon.

The baby rabbits will not come out of the hole. They do not see Mother Rabbit. "Come out of there at once," says Mother Rabbit. "Yes, Mother," say the baby rabbits.

"Come with me," says
Mother Rabbit. "We are
going home."
The baby rabbits look very
sad.
"What were they trying to
do?" say the bees.
"They were trying to hum,
like us," says Dragon.

"We can show them how
to hum," say the bees.
"Yes," says Dragon.
It takes a long time to
show a rabbit how to hum.
Dragon tries very hard.
So do the bees.
At last they do it.

Dragon is humming.
The bees are humming.
The rabbits are humming.
"I did not know rabbits could hum," says Owl.
"My babies are the only rabbits who can," says Mother Rabbit.

Say these words again

Mother
baby
babies
rabbit
once
something
could

know
bush
listen
trying
where
show
hear

What are they doing?

crying

hopping

peeping

listening

hiding

125